dramascripts

Hijack

a play in one act
by

CHARLES WELLS

M

Macmillan Education
London and Basingstoke

First published 1972
Reprinted 1975, 1976, 1977, 1978, 1980, 1981, 1982, 1983

Published by
MACMILLAN EDUCATION LTD
Houndmills Basingstoke Hampshire RG21 2XS
and London
Associated companies in Delhi Dublin
Hong Kong Johannesburg Lagos Melbourne
New York Singapore and Tokyo

Printed in Hong Kong

FOREWORD

Drama is one of the most exciting of all forms of human activity. At its best, it involves us completely — whether we are acting ourselves or watching others act — and those occasions when we are gripped by some dramatic tension may be among the most memorable moments in our lives. In this new series we hope to encourage this sort of experience.

DRAMASCRIPTS are intended for use in secondary schools, amateur theatrical groups and youth clubs. The plays range widely from established classics to new works and adaptations of books and film scripts. There is nothing in any of the plays that is beyond the capabilities of younger actors. They may be used in a variety of ways: read privately for pleasure or aloud in groups, acted in the classroom, church hall or youth club, or in public performances. The maximum enjoyment is obviously to be found in actual performance — and the benefits of acting need no elaboration — but we have borne in mind that the play must interest and entertain however it is used, and we are confident that even the solitary reader will find here something of the excitement of the live theatre.

GUY WILLIAMS
Advisory Editor

For Mary

PRODUCTION NOTES

The play can be performed equally well on the classroom floor or on a stage. In either case the interior of the aircraft may be represented by a line of chairs, arranged in rows of four, two either side of a central gangway. The door leading to the stewardess's quarters and the passengers' lavatory is at the rear of the plane and the door to the pilot's cabin is, of course, at the front. An exit point must therefore be arranged — perhaps by screens — at either end of the gangway.

The Professor sits towards the front of the plane and Miss Pringle sits near him on the opposite side of the gangway. Behind them sits Travers and behind him Wing-Commander Fanshaw and his wife. A couple of rows further back still sit the three schoolboys, Peter nearest the window. The chess-players sit together somewhere about the middle of the plane. The remaining seats should, as far as possible, be occupied by other passengers, who may, for the sake of verisimilitude, converse quietly among themselves, read or even sleep except where the action of the play demands otherwise.

THE CHARACTERS

PROFESSOR MANNINGTREE, a professor of history
WING-COMMANDER FANSHAW, ex-R.A.F. (very)
ENID FANSHAW, his unobtrusive wife
TRAVERS, a somewhat aggressive business man
MISS MADELEINE PRINGLE, an elderly lady making her first flight
PETER ⎫
STEVE ⎬ schoolboys and classmates
GRAHAM ⎭
CAPTAIN STEWART, the pilot (heard over the loud-speaker)
SHAFTI ⎫ hi-jackers of a 'Middle-Eastern' appearance
MUSTAPHA ⎭
JANET DAVIDSON, the stewardess
1st CHESS PLAYER
2nd CHESS PLAYER

OTHER PASSENGERS

HIJACK

(The action takes place in the passenger section of a transatlantic airliner in flight)

Captain Stewart's voice over the loud-speaker. Ladies and gentlemen, this is your pilot, Captain Stewart, speaking. You may now unfasten your seatbelts and smoke if you wish to. We are flying at 15,000 feet, and if you look down to your right you can see the River Thames, with Windsor Castle on the nearer side. Our estimated time of arrival at Kennedy International Airport is 6.30 p.m. G.M.T. or 1.30 p.m. local time. Your stewardess, Miss Janet Davidson, will be pleased to give you any further information you may require. Finally, on behalf of the crew, may I wish you an enjoyable trip.

Miss Pringle *(nervously to Fanshaw).* Excuse me. I'm so sorry to trouble you, but you see I've never flown before. I know the captain said we could undo our seatbelts, but don't you think it might be better if I kept mine on? If the plane has to brake suddenly or . . .

Fanshaw. Madam, I can assure you that you will be perfectly safe without your seatbelt. It isn't like being in a car you know. Between us and New York are three thousand miles of more-or-less-empty sky. I don't think you need to worry about collisions. Mind you, when I was in Spitfires it was a different story. Over the Straits of Dover some nights it was like Piccadilly Circus in the rush hour. Here, let me help you with that. *(He gets up and helps Miss Pringle to unfasten the belt)*

Miss Pringle. Oh thank you so much Mr. . . . er . . .

Fanshaw. Fanshaw, Wing-Commander Fanshaw actually. This is my wife, Enid. Enid's a seasoned air-traveller now, aren't you my

1

dear?

Mrs. Fanshaw *(without looking up from her knitting)*. Yes, dear.

Miss Pringle. And do you enjoy flying, Mrs. Fanshaw?

Fanshaw. Oh yes. You wouldn't travel any other way, would you my dear?

Mrs. Fanshaw. No, dear.

Travers. Stewardess!

Miss Davidson. Just one moment sir. *(She is busy attending to another passenger)*

Travers *(to the world at large)*. I don't know what this line's coming to. At one time you used to get some service.

Miss Davidson *(politely)*. I can only attend to one person at a time sir. *(She walks briskly down the gangway and exits)*

Travers. Dammit. This *is* a British plane, isn't it?

1st Chess Player. Check!

Travers. What's that? Czech did you say? I thought this was B.O.A.C. flight 702 to New York! Don't say I'm on the wrong plane! I've got an important business conference at three this afternoon. Where are we going to, then, Prague?

1st Chess Player. Mate in two, I think.

2nd Chess Player. No, if I move this bishop . . .

Professor Manningtree *(gently)*. There's no need to worry sir. This *is* the B.O.A.C. flight to New York. This gentleman didn't say 'Czech' you see, he said 'check'.

Travers. Afraid I don't follow you, old boy.

2

Professor. You see he's playing chess. 'Check' is a term used in that game.

Travers. Chess? Waste of time if you ask me. Never could see the sense in playing games when there were more profitable ways of spending one's time. I started work when I was fourteen you know. Had to make my own way in the world. I wouldn't have been in my present position if I'd wasted time like young people do nowadays. They get too much for nothing if you ask me. Take all this free education, for instance. *I* never went to university and *I've* got on well enough. I'm in shoes, by the way. What's *your* line, may I ask?

Professor. I'm at Oxford. Professor of Renaissance History, actually.

(The stewardess approaches as they talk)

Travers *(unabashed).* Oh. History, eh? Never had much time for that myself. Bit of a waste of . . .

Miss Davidson. What would you like, sir?

Travers. Oh, there you are. Double whisky and soda. Will you join me, Professor?

Professor. Well that's very civil of you . . .

(Their conversation continues inaudibly)

Peter *(looking out of the window).* What do you reckon that is, Steve? Look. Down there.

Steve. Must be a motorway. Yes, look, there's a lorry.

Peter. You can see the driver's arm out of the cab window. Fantastic.

Graham. You can't see that from up here.

Peter. Yes, honestly.

3

Steve. He's probably flicking the ash off his fag.

Graham. Come on, hawk-eye. What brand is it? Players or Senior Service? What make's his wrist-watch? Can't you see? It's usually written just under the twelve.

Peter. There's cloud there now. I doubt whether we'll see much more.

Steve. We'll be over the sea soon anyway.

Graham. Gets boring, doesn't it? I wish we were on one of those planes that have films. I was on one last Easter. Saw 'The Caine Mutiny'. Jolly good it was. All about this bloke who . . .

Peter
Steve } *(in unison).* We've *seen* it.

Graham. I wish something interesting would happen.

Peter. Like what, for instance?

Graham. Well, maybe we could crash-land on a desert island like in *Lord of the Flies.*

Steve *(staring intently out of the window).* Don't speak too soon, Graham, I think the wing's on fire. Look!

Peter *(excitedly).* Yeah! Look at those flames!

Graham *(leaping up agitatedly).* Where? Where?

(Peter and Steve collapse back in their seats, pointing at Graham and roaring with laughter. Graham realises he has been made to look foolish and takes a playful punch at Steve. A friendly fight ensues, and the boys end up rolling in the gangway. It is soon quelled by angry looks and mutterings from their fellow passengers)

Peter *(breathlessly).* We really had him going then, Steve. Did you see his face? Pretty well reaching for his parachute.

4

Steve. Parachute? You don't think our Graham would abandon a sinking plane do you? He'd crawl along the wing and smother the flames with his hankie.

Graham *(deciding to join in the joke).* No. I'd take over the controls, put her into a dive, bring her right down over the sea, dip the wing in and then pull her nose up just before she ditched.

Fanshaw *(who has been listening amusedly to the conversation).* That's the stuff lad. Reminds me of when my Spitfire ran into flak over Calais. *(He pauses to light his pipe)* Started to lose fuel. Suddenly these two Messerschmitts came at me out of the sun. By the time I'd shaken them off I didn't have enough juice to reach Dover. I had to decide whether to bale out or try to bring her down in the drink.

Graham *(agog).* What did you do?

Fanshaw. Well, the Channel was a bit choppy but I thought I could . . .

Miss Pringle *(who has got out of her seat and is tapping him on the shoulder).* Excuse me, Wing-Commander. I'm sorry to trouble you again, but you see I'm not used to aeroplanes.

Fanshaw *(slightly irritated at the interruption to his story).* Yes, yes, what can I do for you?

Miss Pringle. I've been thinking about what the pilot said just now. He said we would arrive at New York at lunch-time, didn't he?

Fanshaw. Yes, that's right. Half-past one.

Miss Pringle. Well I know this sounds silly, but it's a quarter to one already, and I'm sure the man at the airport said the journey took six hours.

Fanshaw. Yes, but you see the time in New York is five hours behind the time in London. So we leave London at lunch-time and get to New York in time for another lunch.

5

Miss Pringle. Oh dear. This is all very confusing. Will it be lunch-time yesterday or lunch-time tomorrow? You see I've had my lunch already. I had a lamb chop at my sister's.

Fanshaw *(sighing)*. No, no. It'll still be today. Look, let me put it this way. If this plane were twice as fast and we could cross the Atlantic in three hours instead of six then we would reach New York two hours before we left London.

*(**Miss Pringle** looks hopelessly confused)*

At least, we wouldn't *really* get there before we started, but because of this time-difference we gain an extra five hours. Let me give you another example. Suppose we were flying to America the *long* way round. When we crossed the date-line we would go forward a day so today would be the 19th instead of the 18th.

Miss Pringle. Oh dear, oh dear! Today is my nephew's birthday, and I was so looking forward to giving him his present when he meets me at the airport. I've knitted him a lovely mauve pullover and now it seems I'll be too late.

Fanshaw *(exasperated, under his breath)*. Never mind, you can always give it to him for Christmas.

Captain Stewart's voice over the loud-speaker. Ladies and gentlemen, this is Captain Stewart speaking. We are now over the Atlantic Ocean and flying at 30,000 feet. The weather in New York is warm and sunny. Seventy-eight degrees to be exact. Flying conditions are perfect and we may well arrive a few minutes early. *(The loud-speaker clicks off)*

*(A swarthy passenger, **Mustapha**, who has been sitting inconspicuously near the back of the plane, walks down the gangway and through the doorway marked 'Crew Only' leading to the pilot's cabin. The stewardess hurries down the gangway after him)*

Miss Davidson *(shouting)*. Excuse me, sir, you're going the wrong way. You're not allowed in there!

6

(Before she can pursue him through the doorway **Shafti** *springs to his feet, brandishing a large pistol)*

Shafti. Stop! I am holding a gun! Sit down please. Ladies and gentlemen, this airplane has been seized in the name of the People's Republic of El Shiraz. Please not to panic. Remain in your sittings and nobody will be damaged.

(There is a moment of stunned silence. Then everybody starts to speak at once. Through the hubub the following remarks can be heard)

Travers. This is outrageous! This is a *British* plane, sir!

Fanshaw. Look here old man. There are women and children on board y'know. *(To his wife)* Steady on, Enid old girl.

Mrs. Fanshaw *(continuing to knit)*. Yes dear.

Steve. This is fantastic!

Peter. What a story to tell them back at school.

Graham. Just like this film I saw. 'Sky Pirates' it was called. There was this bloke who . . .

Peter
Steve } *(in unison)*. We've *seen* it!

Miss Pringle *(to Fanshaw)*. Excuse me. I do beg your pardon but this is so new to me. There's a gentleman standing over there and he's holding something in his hand that looks awfully like a pistol. We haven't got to New York yet have we? My sister Millicent says that everyone in America carries a pistol. She has a television, you see. I know it's supposed to take three-quarters of an hour but the captain did say we might be early, didn't he? Has the plane stopped?

1st Chess Player. Check mate.

Shafti. What is that you are saying?

Professor *(helpfully).* He said 'check mate'.

Shafti. Why are you calling me 'mate'? My country and yours are enemies. I am not your mate. Fifteen of my countrymen are in British prisons. That is why we have overtaken your plane. We will not let you go until our brave freedom fighters are back on Shirazi dirt.

Professor *(helpful still).* Soil.

Shafti. Thank you. Yes. Soil. *(He is standing at one end of the gangway and watching the passengers warily, gun waving menacingly from side to side)*

Travers. But dammit man, this plane will be in New York in five hours' time, so how can . . .

Shafti *(interrupting).* Oh no, my English mate. In less than five hours this plane will be in El Shiraz.

Travers. This is preposterous. I have a very important business conference this afternoon. I absolutely refuse to go to . . . to . . .

Professor *(helpfully again).* El Shiraz.

Travers. We refuse, I tell you.

Shafti. But I am pointing the gun. I am holding – how do you say it? – all the trumpets.

Professor. Trumps.

Shafti. Thank you. Yes. Trumps.

Captain Stewart's voice over the loudspeaker. Ladies and gentlemen. This is Captain Stewart speaking. May I have your attention please. As you must be aware by now, a most regrettable incident has occurred. However I can assure you that there is absolutely no cause for alarm. I want all of you to do exactly as Mr. Shafti says. On no account is anybody to attempt to disarm him. Such an action could conceivably jeopardise the safety of us all. I'm afraid I have no option but to obey Mr. Mustapha, who is here in the cockpit with me now, and to turn the plane and head back in the direction from which we have come. It goes without saying that I deeply regret having to take such action, but I can assure you that I am left with no alternative. Please co-operate with Mr. Shafti as far as is reasonably possible. Remember there is absolutely no danger so long as you do so. I will give you further information in due course. Thank you. *(The loud-speaker clicks off)*

Fanshaw. This is disgraceful. Stewart's an ex-R.A.F. chap. Bomber Command. Got no right to give such an order. Duty of every officer to try to escape when in the hands of the enemy. When I was a prisoner of war back in . . .

Miss Davidson. Ladies and gentlemen. With Mr. Shafti's permission, and bearing in mind what the Captain has just said, I will be coming round with coffee and sandwiches in a few minutes.

Travers. Make mine a double whisky and soda.

Fanshaw. Think I'll join you old boy.

Shafti. No you must stay where you are please. All except the waitress must remain in his seats.

Steve. Have you got an atlas in your bag, Graham?

Graham. I think so, why?

Steve. I want to see where this El Shiraz place is.

Graham *(finding atlas).* Sounds like the Middle-East. Yes, here it is. Page 16.

Peter *(looking over his shoulder and pointing).* Look. There it is. On the Red Sea.

Steve. Not very big, is it?

Graham. Hardly big enough for an air-field by the look of it.

Peter. Well we'll have to come down *somewhere*, that's for sure.

Steve. Unless all the engines fail and we're stuck up here.

(The other two boys laugh at this. As the laughter dies down we hear . . .)

Miss Pringle. You know, Wing-Commander, this gets more and more puzzling. The captain said we were turning round didn't he? Well when we get back to London what time will it be? Will it be the day *after* tomorrow? You see my sister Millicent visits her niece in Hampshire on Fridays and I have to feed the cat. He's a blue Persian you know.

Fanshaw. Sounds like Mr. Shafti — though come to think of it I should imagine he's more of a *red* Persian, what? *(He chuckles at his own cleverness)*

Professor *(who does not share Fanshaw's sense of humour).* Actually, Wing-Commander, Persia's over a thousand miles from El Shiraz.

Travers. These countries are all the same. No respect for the Union Jack any more, any of them. Pity we closed down our bases over there. A couple of infantry battalions would soon stop their little game.

Fanshaw. Infantry? No, a fighter squadron would do the trick in half the time. These foreign chappies soon take to their heels when a couple of dozen Phantoms open up on them. I remember one afternoon near Tobruk . . .

(His voice fades into the background and we hear those of the two chess players *who have been quietly getting on with their game, oblivious, apparently, of the events of the preceding few minutes)*

1st Chess Player. A good move. You have my rook. By the way wasn't that the captain's voice over the loudspeaker just now?

10

2nd Chess Player. Was it? I heard nothing.

1st Chess Player. Well it can't have been anything important. Now it's my move I believe. How can I escape?

Shafti *(Jerking to attention at the word 'escape'. His concentration has been wandering a little. Standing pointing a gun can soon get tiring).* What are you saying? Escape? There shall be no escaping. You will all remain in our fingers until the British Government releases my fellow-countrymen.

Professor. Didn't you people hijack a *Swiss* plane a few weeks ago?

Shafti. Yes. The passengers are now in goal in Shiraz.

Graham. You mean they're *playing football* out there?

Professor. I think Mr. Shafti means they're in *gaol.*

Shafti. Gaol. Yes, that is the word. And they are staying there until the Swiss Government pays us back the money it has stolen from us.

Professor. How did the Swiss come to steal money from you?

Shafti. For many years my country has been ruled by Sheikh Suleiman. But last year we were revolting . . .

Fanshaw *(aside to* **Travers***).* You're still pretty repulsive *this* year if you ask me.

Shafti. . . . and Sheikh Suleiman was shot. When we tried to get back all the money he had gathered — money that belongs to the people of Shiraz — we found that he had put it in a bank in Switzerland. The Swiss Government refuses to repay it. So we blow up their plane and lock up their passengers. And now we wait.

Travers. And what, may I ask, do you propose to do with *us* if we ever reach your country?

Shafti. You will be locked up too. Until your Government releases the fifteen Shirazi liberation fighters that are in your prisons.

Travers. And what were they put in prison *for*?

Shafti. They have been blowing up oil pipe-lines over the border in Quatan, which is still a British colony.

Fanshaw. I'm glad to hear we've still got one left. The last government must have forgotten all about that one.

Miss Davidson *(as she distributes drinks)*. But surely, Mr. Shafti, if these men went round deliberately blowing up pipe-lines in another country they can hardly complain about being punished.

Shafti *(warming to his theme)*. But you see the pipe was carrying away *our* oil — oil belonging to the people of El Shiraz. It was carrying it to the sea to be shipped off by a British company.

Travers. But dammit man, the company was paying you for the oil, wasn't it?

Shafti *(triumphantly)*. Ah, but you see the money was going not to the Shirazi people but into the Swiss bank of Sheikh Suleiman.

Professor. Which is where we came in, I think.

Miss Pringle. Yes, that's right. This is the door we came in by. I remember distinctly. Are we supposed to go out by the same door? *(She stands up)* I must hurry back to my sister's and feed the cat.

Shafti. Please be sitting down madam.

Miss Pringle. I beg your pardon, young man, but I am most anxious to get off the plane as soon as possible. Have the stairs been put in position yet? *(She looks about her in confusion)*

Fanshaw. I'm afraid they'll need to be pretty long ones, we're still at 30,000 feet.

Miss Pringle. I thought we were back in London. Really this is all *most* confusing.

Professor *(gently).* I'm afraid this is going to come as rather a shock to you. Will you listen very carefully? This plane is now on its way to El Shiraz, a small country on the Red Sea.

Miss Pringle. But this is B.O.A.C. flight 702 to New York. I was *most* careful to get on the right plane. I remember once catching what I thought was the Manchester train and arriving in Plymouth. You see I was there at the right time and I was on the right platform but I'd gone to Paddington instead of Euston. Ever since then I've been *so* careful.

Professor. Yes, this *is* the New York plane — or at least it *was. (A look of total non-comprehension suffuses* **Miss Pringle's** *face)* I'm afraid we've been hijacked. That young man with the gun in his hand has made the pilot turn the plane round and take us to El Shiraz.

Miss Pringle. You know I *thought* that was a gun, but I've got my *reading* glasses on, you see, and I wasn't quite sure. I'm afraid I've always had rather poor eyesight. The other day I was in the bank writing a . . .

1st Chess Player. Check!

Miss Pringle *(puzzled).* No, actually I think it was a paying-in form, but it doesn't really affect the story . . . *(*Miss Davidson *puts an end to the anecdote with a cup of coffee)*

Graham *(quietly, to the other boys).* I bet it wouldn't be very difficult to get hold of old Shafti's gun.

Steve. What do you suggest?

Graham. Well in Westerns the hero usually creeps up on the bad guy, behind a rock or something, and then throws some pebbles to distract his attention. Then as soon as . . .

Peter. Have you got a pile of pebbles handy then?

13

Graham. It doesn't have to be pebbles, you nit. Anything will do.

Steve *(sarcastically).* That's right. Why not a few cushions lobbed over his head? Or what about a couple of suitcases?

Peter *(still more sarcastically).* Come to that, if you wanted to be really clever, you could go up to him, stare over his shoulder and say 'Grab him men!' He spins round and you dive for his gun. I doubt whether anyone's ever tried that one.

Steve. These hijackers aren't idiots you know. They're not going to fall for some stupid trick that Gary Cooper pulled in 'High Noon'.

Graham. Hey, did you *see* 'High Noon'? Do you remember that bit when . . .

Peter
Steve } *(in unison).* Yes, we *saw* it.

Peter. Graham's got a point though, seriously. Are we all just going to sit here and let *one* bloke take the whole lot of us to the middle of the Sahara Desert or wherever it is?

Graham. It isn't one bloke it's *two*. There's another one in the cockpit, remember.

Steve. And El Shiraz is nowhere near the Sahara, it's . . .

Peter *(irritated, interrupting).* O.K. Never mind where it is. It sounds pretty crummy. We could spend months in some dirty prison out there.

Graham. And if the Government refuses to release those prisoners we could stay there for ever.

Steve. Or be blown up with the plane.

Peter. And it's the Cup Final in a fortnight. Look, if we're going to overpower this Shafti bloke everyone's going to have to work together. We can't do much on our own.

14

Graham. And to do that we've got to find a way of getting the word round to the others without old Shafti cottoning on to what's happening, and that won't be easy.

*(****Shafti*** *strolls slowly towards them, gun still in hand)*

Steve. Shh — he's coming.

Fanshaw *(Quietly, to* **Travers** *and* **Professor Manningtree***).* I think we should try to *do* something. You know, duty of every officer to try to escape and all that. If we're going to get this plane back to London . . .

Travers. London? Back to New York, that's where we're supposed to be going. Remember I may lose a very valuable business contract if I don't get there today.

Fanshaw. All right, New York, but the point is this. Someone's got to show some initiative, take the lead.

Professor. If we could get all — or even some — of the passengers to co-operate I'm sure we could find a way of catching him off his guard and tying him up. Then we'd just have the chap in the cockpit to deal with.

Travers. And we'd have Shafti's gun.

Professor. Even if we can think up a good stratagem we'll need to find a way of letting the others know what's going on without Shafti getting wind of it.

Mrs. Fanshaw *(Everyone shows surprise when she speaks. She does not stop knitting).* If the stewardess were to stumble and tip a tray of drinks over him, that would give someone a chance to grab his pistol and sit on him.

Fanshaw. I say, that's not a bad idea old girl. It might just work.

Professor. But it's got to be carefully thought out. We've got to decide who's going to do the actual grappling. And we've got to have a

15

pre-arranged signal.

Fanshaw. Well, as it was my idea . . .

2nd Chess Player. Check!

Professor *(Excitedly, raising his voice for a second but quickly lowering it again as* **Shafti** *glances in his direction).* That's it! Of course! Check! Those chess players have been saying 'check' at odd intervals ever since we left London. That's the perfect signal. Shafti won't suspect a thing.

Travers. Wait a minute. Supposing one of the *real* chess players says it at the wrong moment.

Professor. We'll just have to make sure he doesn't. We must find a way of communicating with the others as unobtrusively as possible.

Fanshaw. Not forgetting the stewardess of course. But that should be easy enough. Shafti doesn't seem to mind her continuing to serve people. I'll call her over and order something. Then while she's serving me I'll put her in the picture.

Travers. Do you think she'll agree?

Professor. I don't imagine she's any keener to rot in some sordid Shirazi gaol than the rest of us are. I think she'll co-operate.

(
Shafti *walks towards them)*

Fanshaw. Look out — Shafti's coming this way. *(They break off their discussion and look nonchalant)*

Steve *(to the other two boys).* I know. One of us goes along the gangway as if going to the lavatory, and just as he's going past old Shafti he trips over and knocks into him. The other two be ready to grab the gun. He's bound to be off balance for a moment.

Graham. It's a bit risky, isn't it? Supposing the gun goes off?

16

Peter. Well if *you* bump into him hard enough, and if Steve and I and some of the others are ready to jump on him at exactly the right moment I reckon it should work.

Graham *(aghast)*. Me? Why *me?*

Steve. He'll never suspect you. You look too feeble to punch your way out of a paper bag.

Graham *(indignantly)*. I beat you in the cross-country last term.

Steve. Only because I stopped off for a cup of tea at Slimy Joe's. Anyway the *dangerous* part is grabbing the gun.

Peter. We'll have to have a signal so that everyone can be ready.

Steve. And it's got to be one that won't mean anything to Jenghiz Khan.

Graham. Who?

Steve. Shafti, you twit!

Graham. I know. Everyone can see that clock at the end. Let's make it when the minute hand reaches half-past.

Peter. Apart from the fact that *you* thought of it that's not a bad idea. I'll write it down on a piece of paper and pass it round the plane.

Graham. Shafti might see it.

Steve. Not if we're careful. Look, there's some special air-line notepaper on this shelf. *(He hands a piece to* **Peter** *who begins to write)*

*(***Fanshaw*** *beckons over the stewardess and they have a whispered conversation.* **Shafti** *has relaxed a bit and takes little notice.* **Miss Davidson** *goes about her business)*

Fanshaw *(to* **Professor Manningtree** *and* **Travers**). O.K. It's on. All we've

17

got to do now is to let as many of the others know as possible.

Professor. If we scribbled a note, perhaps we could manage to pass it down the plane without our gun-toting friend being any the wiser.

Travers. It's worth a try. Here's some airline notepaper *(he hands a sheet to the* **Professor***)*. Scribble a few lines on this and fold it over.

Fanshaw. Don't forget to mention that signal I thought up.

Professor. Right. Leave it to me. *(He begins to write)*

Peter *(to* **Steve** *and* **Graham***)*. There, that should be clear enough.

Steve. Fold it over. Now, pass it up towards the front — quick, while Shafti's looking the other way. *(***Peter** *passes it to the passenger in front, telling him in a low voice to read it and pass it on)*

Graham. If this works out the note should get back to us eventually. *(He looks up towards the clock)* Not long to go. I'm getting the jitters.

Peter. There's nothing to worry about. You just walk down the gangway, trip over your own feet — which shouldn't be difficult in your case — and barge into him. We'll do the rest — Steve, me and the other passengers in that bit of the plane.

(During this and the following dialogue **Peter's** *note is being passed slowly along the line of seats, each recipient waiting his moment before handing it on.* **Shafti***, quite relaxed now, leans against a seat a the further end of the gangway, gun dangling loosely from his hand. He is clearly oblivious of what is afoot)*

Professor. There, that should do the trick. I've spelt it out in words of one syllable. When I call out 'check' Miss Davidson will come down the gangway with a loaded tray and stumble into Shafti. In the confusion those nearest will grab hold of him and the rest of us will pile in on top. *(He folds the note over and, after a surreptitious glance at* **Shafti***, whose attention is elsewhere, he*

18

passes it back, whispering to the recipient to pass it round the plane. During the next few moments the **Professor's** *note is slowly passed in the opposite direction to* **Peter's,** *and they cross)*

Travers. When the note gets back here we'll know everyone's seen it.

Fanshaw. I say, I'm getting quite excited. Reminds me of when I was at Biggin Hill, waiting for the balloon to go up.

Travers. Balloon? I thought you flew *Spitfires* not *balloons*. But do you think it will work? I really would hate to miss that conference.

Professor. I think it's got a good chance. I just hope the gun doesn't go off in the struggle. Still, I think it's a justifiable risk if you balance it against what might happen if we land in El Shiraz. *(A passenger hands him* **Peter's** *note)* Well, that note got round quickly.

Travers. Shafti's looking this way. Better screw it up and put it in your pocket. *(The Professor does so without looking at it)*

Professor. Right. We're all set then.

Graham *(Receiving* **The Professor's** *note from the next passenger).* Peter, the note's got back.

Peter. Wow, that didn't take long.

Steve. Better destroy it. *(Graham crumples it up without giving it a second glance. The paper being identical, it never occurs to him that it is anything but the note that* **Peter** *had written)* Now everyone should know what's going to happen. There's a minute to go. Get ready, Graham.

Peter. Remember, all you've got to do is to knock him off balance for a split second. The rest of us will be on him like a ton of bricks. He won't know what hit him.

(Shafti is now standing in the middle of the gangway, completely off his guard)

19

Steve. Give it just a few more seconds, just to make sure everyone's seen the clock. Now!

(Graham stands up and moves into the gangway. Shafti tenses and looks at him suspiciously)

Graham *(trying to sound casual).* Just going to the lavatory.

(Shafti relaxes again. Graham walks towards him)

Professor. Check! *(From the opposite direction Miss Davidson moves down the gangway towards Shafti carrying a tray piled with plates and glasses. Shafti gives her a quick glance but has no reason to suspect anything. As they near Shafti both Graham and Miss Davidson quicken their pace slightly. At the last possible split-second Shafti realises their intentions and springs aside. Both already committed to their actions, Graham and Miss Davidson pitch forward and collide headlong, the tray and its contents flying into the air. At the same moment a number of other passengers, including Travers, Fanshaw, Peter and Steve, already on their feet and moving a second or two earlier, dive into the confused mêlée. Shafti stands back and watches open mouthed as the heap of bodies sorts itself out and people disentangle themselves)*

Graham *(from the bottom of the heap, in a muffled voice).* Get off! Get off! I'm suffocating!

(The 'wrestlers' eventually stand up, dusting themselves down and rubbing their injured parts. They look sheepishly at one another. Graham, the last to surface, removes food and broken crockery from his person)

Shafti *(agitatedly).* Back to your sittings, all of you. *(He waves the gun wildly)* Do not try such a thing again I am warning you.

(The other hijacker, Mustapha, appears in the cockpit doorway, gun in hand. He and Shafti exchange a few words in a foreign language, perhaps Arabic. Mustapha goes back into the cockpit, closing the door behind him. By this time all the passengers are

back in their seats)

Miss Pringle *(to* **Fanshaw***)*. Excuse me, Wing-Commander, but why did all those people fall over in the gangway just now? We haven't landed yet, have we? I don't remember being told to fasten my seat-belt. What time is it in Algiers?

Fanshaw. El Shiraz, not Algiers, Miss . . . er . . .

Miss Pringle. Pringle — Madeleine Pringle.

Professor. Well you see, Miss Pringle, the Wing-Commander and I had what we thought was a good idea for overpowering the hijacker and taking his gun away from him.

Travers. Unfortunately that horrible little schoolboy mucked it up. If he hadn't got in the way our friend Mr. Shafti would have been nicely trussed up by now.

Miss Pringle. Oh dear, oh dear, I do wish I'd taken Millicent's advice and travelled by sea. But my nephew tells me that this is the only way to cross the Atlantic these days — nobody goes by boat any more.

Fanshaw. Quite right. Quite right, eh, Enid?

Mrs. Fanshaw *(knitting)*. Yes, dear.

Peter *(to* **Graham***)*. Well, you made a right mess of that, didn't you?

Graham. I like that! How was *I* to know the stewardess would come charging along with that tray?

Steve *(sarcastically)*. You were supposed to bump into the hijacker, not the stewardess. The hijacker's the one with the gun. The stewardess is the one wearing the skirt.

Peter. When we get back to London . . .

Steve. *If* we get back to London.

Peter. . . . you ought to apply for a job with M.I.5, Graham.

Steve. Yes, I saw an ad. in yesterday's paper. 'Wanted, bright young lad. Judo black belt and degree in ballistics an advantage but not essential. Must be able to make tea'. You can just see him, can't you Pete? Agent 008 Graham Jones, licensed to suck wine gums.

Peter. And carry a water-pistol. Unloaded, of course.

Steve *(in a mock-dramatic voice)*. Big X sits behind his desk in his Whitehall office — back to the camera, of course — 'A dangerous mission, this. Better send for 008'.

Peter *(in a falsetto voice)*. 008 here sir!

Steve. This one could get a little nasty, Jones. I've no right to *order* you to go, but . . .

Peter *(still falsetto)*. That's O.K. sir. I know the form. You can rely on me, Big X.

Steve. Look, 008. I'll come straight to the point. I want you to parachute into the Kremlin, capture the Supreme Soviet, and bring them back alive. You'll need to take some string and a penknife. Afraid you'll have to swim back, Jones, can't afford to release transport, there's a big thing on at White Hart Lane. Look, here's ten pence — swim up the Thames to Tower Bridge and then get the Tube. Any questions, 008?

Peter. Only one sir.

Steve. Yes?

Peter. Will you be needing me this afternoon as well? *(The two of them curl up in helpless laughter at their own wit)*

Graham. O.K. Very funny. You two were a lot of help, weren't you, piling on top of *me*. About the only person in the plane who *didn't* sit on my head was old Shafti.

22

Steve. You shouldn't have such a comfortable head. *(more laughter.)*

Captain Stewart's voice over the loud-speaker. Ladies and gentlemen, this is Captain Stewart. May I have your attention please. We are now over the Mediterranean, and I anticipate landing at the Shiraz airstrip in about three-quarters of an hour. I will then be permitted to make radio contact with London to arrange for your relatives to be informed of the situation. Will you please write down the names, addresses and, where possible, the 'phone numbers of those you wish to be notified. The stewardess will collect them. Let me reassure you that there is no cause for alarm. The airstrip at Shiraz is perfectly adequate for this type of aircraft, and though the landing may be a trifle bumpier than at Heathrow you may rest assured that it will be perfectly normal. Once we are down we will be in the hands of the . . . er . . . Shirazi Revolutionary Council who will be in constant touch with the Government in London. I'm sure it will not be long before we are permitted to leave. Thank you. *(The loudspeaker clicks off)*

Professor. He's whistling to keep our spirits up. I can't see them letting us go in a hurry.

Fanshaw. Those Swissair passengers have been held prisoner for over a month, haven't they?

Professor. Yes, I believe so.

Shafti *(brandishing his pistol).* You have all heard what your captain has said. In a few minutes now you will be in the People's Republic of El Shiraz. You will be well looked at there.

Professor. Looked *after.*

Shafti. Thank you. Yes. Looked *after.*

Fanshaw *(quietly).* Probably well looked *at* as well. I know these chappies. Met 'em in the war. Sight of an Englishman they all come crowding round staring and trying to sell you postcards.

Travers. They won't get much change out of me, I can tell you. *(He*

23

pauses) Wait a minute. Do they wear shoes these native fellows?

Fanshaw. I dare say some of them own the odd sandal or two, why?

Travers *(brightening)*. Might be a chance for me to do a business deal after all. I say . . . er . . . Mr. Shafti . . .

Shafti *(approaching suspiciously)*. What are you wanting?

Travers. I wondered whether your . . . *(he hesitates, then pronounces the next word with some difficulty)* . . . government might be interested in a large consignment of shoes I happen to have available. Best quality leather, complete range of sizes. Could arrange to have them shipped out to your place . . .

Shafti. Shoes? *(as though reciting from a pamphlet)* The people of my country in their heroic struggle against the forces of imperialism have no need of *shoes*. Shoes to us are a symbol of the decadence of Western society. *(In a different tone)* Now if it is a question of *guns* . . .

Travers *(hesitantly at first)*. Well . . . a friend of mine in Birmingham does a nice little line in machine-pistols. I think it's possible that . . .

Shafti *(beaming)*. Ah! Now we are — how do you say it? — cooking with oil.

Professor. Gas. Tell me, Mr. Shafti, have you lived in England? You seem, if I may say so, to have a remarkable grasp of our language and its idiom.

Shafti *(pleased)*. Oh yes! I was for two years at your London School of Economics.

Fanshaw *(aside)*. At *our* expense, no doubt! Fine thing when the British tax-payer pays out good money to train you foreign chappies to steal our oil and hijack our planes . . .

Professor *(who has heard the remark, though Shafti appears not to have done).* I don't think even the London School of Economics runs a degree course in hijacking yet, Wing-Commander. I know one can take a degree in most subjects these days . . .

Travers *(in a markedly more friendly manner).* Tell me, how did you enjoy your two years in London, Mr. Shafti?

Shafti *(relaxing now).* London is a fine city, that I am not denying, but your English winter, it seems to last for eleven months. In my bed-sitting-room in Hackney was this very little fire with this very enormous appetite for ten-penny pieces. That fire was better fed than I was. What my landlady cooked for me I would not give to my uncle's camel — and the camel is eating almost anything I am telling you. But so many fine buildings and statues there are in London. Especially I like Napoleon's Column in Trafalgar Square, and that statue of one of your kings outside the Parliament — Richard the Cowardly Lion I believe I heard someone call him, though he is looking brave enough to me, waving his scimitar in the sky up there on his horse. And your underground! It is more quickly by pipe as you Londoners say — like our oil, is it not so? In my country the girls show only their eyes, but in London . . .

Travers *(interrupting).* This friend of mine in Birmingham, Mr. Shafti, that I was telling you about. Remarkably decent fellow he is, actually. Owes me a favour as a matter of fact. I think I could persuade him to let you have a few crates of those machine-pistols for only . . . well, if I twist his arm, let's say . . . *(He and* **Shafti** *converse quietly to one side)*

Fanshaw *(making conversation).* Well we won't forget this trip in a hurry, Professor.

*(***Travers** *and* **Shafti** *pass down the gangway out of earshot, deep in conversation)*

Professor. Good lord, Wing-Commander, I think you may have given me an idea. *(To* **Mrs. Fanshaw***)* May I ask what you're knitting Mrs. Fanshaw?

Mrs. Fanshaw *(surprised).* A balaclava helmet for Cyril — he feels the

25

cold so in his ears poor thing, don't you dear?

Fanshaw *(not pleased).* So you keep telling me, my dear.

Professor. May I borrow the ball of wool for a moment? *(He takes it and examines it closely to the bewilderment of the* Fanshaws*)* Good thick stuff this. *(Almost to himself)* If one were to twist two or three strands together it would be pretty strong . . . in fact strong enough not to break if someone were to run into it.

Fanshaw. I say old man, I think I'm beginning to see what you're driving at.

Professor. If we could tie it across the gangway at about ankle height and pull it nice and taut, then anyone coming along at anything above a slow walk would be almost bound to go flat on his face.

Fanshaw. He'd never see it at that height, especially this dark grey colour. We just have to wait until he's not looking and then rig it up quickly.

Professor. It's not quite as simple as that. We have to find some way of getting him up here at a brisk pace. We can't afford to bungle it a second time, we'll be touching down soon.

Travers *(who has just rejoined them,* Shafti *having remained at the further end of the gangway).* What's all this?

Fanshaw. I've had another idea.

Professor. We're going to fix a trip wire — a trip *wool* actually — for your friend Mr. Shafti. If he takes a tumble over this he's bound to let go of the gun. Once we've got that we must have a good chance of dealing with his friend before we land in Shiraz.

Fanshaw *(to his wife).* Twist together some wool, Enid, treble thickness. We'll need some to tie him up with as well. *(Mrs. Fanshaw busies herself with the wool)*

Travers. Wait a minute. Aren't we taking a bit of a risk? I mean

26

supposing the gun goes off? He doesn't seem a bad sort of a fellow when you get to know him a bit. I think the best thing to do is to wait until we land, and then . . .

Professor. I thought you had an urgent appointment in New York?

Travers. Yes, well I . . . er . . . I mean I'm just thinking of the safety of the passengers, you understand. I'm sure that once we are in Shiraz we could do some kind of a deal with . . . *(he tails off under withering looks from the* **Professor** *and* **Fanshaw***)*

Fanshaw. Quick, while Shafti's looking the other way.

Captain Stewart's voice over the loud-speaker *(While he speaks* **Fanshaw** *and the* **Professor** *tie the wool across the gangway)* Ladies and gentlemen, this is Captain Stewart speaking. If you look down to your right you can see the Red Sea and the Arabian coast. We should be over El Shiraz in about fifteen minutes. *(The loud-speaker clicks off)*

Fanshaw. Fifteen minutes. No time to lose. We must find a way to get Shafti up to this end — and at the double.

Professor. Leave that to me. I'll make a move for the cockpit door. He's bound to rush up here to stop me.

Travers. Supposing he shoots?

Professor. That's a chance I'll have to take — but I'm pretty sure he won't. You two get ready to grab his gun and tie him up. Better gag him too. Ready?

Travers *(reluctantly).* O.K.

Fanshaw. Roger.

*(***Professor Manningtree** *stands up and makes for the door leading to the pilot's cabin)*

Shafti. Hey! Stop! Go back to your sitting. Stop, I am saying, or I will

27

fire you!

*(Professor Manningtree takes no notice. Brandishing his pistol and
continuing to shout, Shafti hurries up the gangway towards him
and falls headlong over the tautly-stretched wool, giving a
strangled cry as he does so. The gun flies out of his hand and
vanishes. Fanshaw and Travers leap on him. The Professor spins
round and helps them to overpower Shafti, tie and gag him, and
bundle him, still struggling violently, into a pair of empty seats so
that he is out of sight from the front of the plane. A cheer goes up
from the rest of the passengers, several of whom have by now
rendered assistance)*

Fanshaw *(breathless)*. It worked!

Professor. Yes. I hope he enjoyed his trip! *(general laughter)*

Mrs. Fanshaw *(looking up from her knitting)*. Well *done*, Professor!

Steve. Great stuff!

Peter. Put up a good fight, though, didn't he?

Graham. Just like Alan Ladd in 'Shane'.

*(Expressions of approval and congratulation are heard from
various other passengers, several of whom crowd round the
Professor, pat him on the back, shake his hand, and so on. While
this is going on the cockpit door flies open and Mustapha appears,
gun in hand, and extremely agitated)*

Mustapha *(shouting above the din)*. Back in your seats, all of you!
Move! *(Reluctantly those passengers who are on their feet do as he
says)* What is going on? Where is Shafti?

Professor *(aside)*. I'm afraid he's a bit tied up at the moment.

Mustapha. Who has the gun? *(There is a long pause. Nobody speaks.
Everyone looks at everyone else. Mustapha glares at each in turn,
brandishing his pistol wildly)* I am ordering you to speak! Release

28

my friend! Hand over the gun! You cannot get away from this!

Professor *(helpfully)*. *With* this.

Mustapha *(automatically)*. Yes, *with* this. *(Fiercely)* I am warning you. I shall shoot. *(He walks slowly down the gangway, looking from side to side, gun waving menacingly in his fist. Eventually he sees* **Shafti** *still lying trussed up across two seats. He speaks to him briefly in his own language.* **Shafti** *grunts through his gag)* Untie him! *(This to the three boys, who are nearby. They hesitate)* Untie him I say to you. *(He points the gun at them. Slowly and reluctantly they begin to do as he says, but stop as soon as* **Mustapha** *turns back to face the rest of the passengers)* One of you has the gun. Let me have it! In five minutes we shall be in the glorious People's Republic of El Shiraz. I *order* you to hand over the gun.

Miss Pringle. Is this what you are looking for, young man? *(She stands up and holds out Shafti's pistol at arm's length, looking at it distastefully)*

Mustapha *(Relieved, and calmer now)*. Yes. Throw it on the floor please.

Miss Pringle. Young man, I am not in the habit of throwing things.

Mustapha *(momentarily nonplussed)*. But I am telling you to let me have this gun! *(He waves his own gun threateningly)*

Miss Pringle *(Icily)*. I should be grateful if you would refrain from pointing that nasty pistol in my direction. I have a nephew of about your age, and if he were to behave in this disgraceful way I can assure you that I would cut him out of my will immediately. I think, young man, it would be better for all concerned if *you* were to hand over *your* gun to *me*. I feel sure I am speaking for *all* the passengers when I say that we have no wish to go to Algiers across your date-line. As a matter of fact I don't eat dates myself. I've always been given to understand that they are bad for one's teeth. And it is most important to me that today is the eighteenth and not the nineteenth. I've knitted this mauve pullover, you see.

29

(Mustapha clearly does not see. He looks thoroughly confused by this speech, not without reason. He stands uncertainly in the gangway, still pointing the gun in Miss Pringle's direction, but obviously baffled as to what to do next. The rest of the passengers, thoroughly absorbed by this confrontation, look intently from one to the other. The three boys have completely abandoned any pretence of untying Shafti, who remains as he was. There is a tense silence)

Mustapha *(almost desperately)*. You do not seem to understand. You are prisoners of the People's Republic of El Shiraz.

Miss Pringle. Nonsense. We are on our way to New York. Indeed we should have been there by now were it not for this outrageous episode. I think you have delayed us long enough. You have behaved abominably, but if you hand over your pistol we will try to say no more about the matter. *(Mustapha mutters something in his own language. It does not sound complimentary. He makes a move towards Miss Pringle)*

Miss Pringle. Stop where you are. 'Put your hands above your head' I believe is the expression one uses on such occasions. You see my sister Millicent has a television set.

(Mustapha stops, uncertainly, and casts a swift and somewhat bewildered glance about the plane, almost as if seeking support from the other passengers. Nobody speaks. Nobody moves. The only sound is a muffled grunt from the gagged Shafti, now completely forgotten)

Mustapha *(angrily)*. Drop that gun or I fire!

Miss Pringle. How dare you threaten me! I always understood that you Oriental people had a reputation for courtesy and good manners.

(Mustapha makes a sudden rush towards Miss Pringle, clearly intent upon seizing the gun by force. There is a loud bang and Mustapha reels back, clutching his arm. His face exhibits astonishment as much as pain. His gun clatters to the floor and Professor Manningtree retrieves it. Delight and surprise in equal

30

*measure are to be seen on the faces of the passengers — save that
of* **Miss Pringle***, who remains calm and dignified)*

Miss Pringle. Young man, I warned you to keep your distance. Now you
must face the consequences of your reprehensible behaviour.
*(***Professor Manningtree** *and* **Fanshaw** *step forward and seize*
Mustapha*, who has gone down on one knee and is looking ruefully
at his injured arm. He offers no resistance as they lead him to an
empty seat where other passengers stand guard over him)*
Wing-Commander, perhaps you would care to take possession of
this unpleasant object. *(***Fanshaw** *takes the pistol from her and
pockets it.* **Miss Davidson** *hurries along the gangway and through
the doorway to the pilot's cabin just as the loud-speaker clicks on
and we hear . . .)*

Captain Stewart's voice over the loud-speaker. This is Captain Stewart
speaking. Will you please fasten your seatbelts and extinguish all
cigarettes. We are making our approach to the El Shiraz airstrip
and we should touch down in . . . *(He breaks off and a muttered
conversation between himself and* **Miss Davidson** *can be partly
heard — words such as 'gun', 'injured', 'overpowered', and 'safe'
may be picked out. He resumes his speech to the passengers)*
Ladies and gentlemen, you seem to have the advantage over me. I
have just been informed that the plane is now safely back in
British hands. I would like to thank those involved in this dramatic
rescue, especially the gallant lady who, I understand, disarmed the
fellow who has been poking the barrel of his gun into my left ear
for most of the journey. I am now turning the plane and heading
back towards the Mediterranean. We will stop for re-fuelling at
Gibraltar and should reach New York in approximately eight
hours from now. Thank you.

Fanshaw. Dashed fine show, Miss Pringle!

Graham. Yes, jolly well done.

Professor. A splendid performance.

Travers. Just what I've always said. No moral fibre these foreign
fellows. Your Englishman will always come out best in the end.

Mrs. Fanshaw *(pointedly, continuing to knit).* Or your English *woman.*

Travers. Oh, . . . er quite so, quite so.

Professor *(rather coldly).* Pity about your friend in Birmingham, though, eh?

Travers. Birmingham? Oh, . . . er . . . just humouring the fellow, of course. No point upsetting him you know. Thoroughly bad piece of work, obviously. *(He looks at his watch)* Think I should just about make that business conference in New York after all.

Miss Pringle. Excuse me, Wing-Commander, but will it be a *Thursday* in Gibraltar? And will I have to fasten my safety-belt again? I do find all this so confusing.

Fanshaw *(sitting beside her and settling himself for a lengthy session).* Well now, Miss Pringle . . . *(the rest of the conversation is lost)*

Graham. Won't they be jealous back at school when they hear all about this!

Peter. Not half! Reminds me of a film I once saw. What was it called, Steve? *(He nudges him and winks)*

Steve. Oh yes. I know the one you mean. Percy Bloggs in 'Son of Batman Strikes Again'.

Graham *(earnestly).* Hey, I don't think I've seen that one! *(Steve and Peter erupt in laughter)*

Travers *(with another glance at his watch).* Stewardess! *(Miss Davidson comes up)* Drinks all round called for, I think. *(To Professor Manningtree)* Looks as though I'll sell those shoes after all!

1st Chess Player *(who, like his friend, has remained quietly in his seat throughout the flight)* Check mate! *(The neighbouring passengers have moved away towards the free drinks, leaving the Chess Players by themselves)* Well, do we wait until the plane has left Gibraltar?

32

2nd Chess Player. Yes, then we stick to Gonzales' original plan. I take the pilot, you see to the passengers.

1st Chess Player *(looking at his watch).* We should reach Cuba by nine.

2nd Chess Player. Right, comrade. Pawn to Queen 4. Your move. *(As the rest of the passengers noisily celebrate their escape the two* **Chess Players** *quietly resume their game)*